D0192946

LOOK
I'm an Engineer

BRARIES NI
WN FROM STOCK

LIBRARIES NI
WITHDRAWN FROM STOCK

For the grown-ups

This book is full of hands-on activities that will tap straight into your child's natural scientific curiosity and engineering creativity. Each activity is designed to let your child play and learn with all their senses. Together, you can grow their love of science, their engineering ingenuity, and their understanding of the world.

Here are a few tips to help you along the way:

Your child should be supervised at all times when conducting these experiments, but try to give them time and space to lead the direction of play. The questions in this book are suggestions. Let your child ask their own questions, and try out their own ideas.

•

Involve your child in the preparation of each activity. Let them follow the instructions but also let them try out their own ideas and explore the investigations in ways that they find interesting. You never know what they might discover!

•

Adult Alert stars show where your child will need extra grown-up help.

•

Protect the area where your child will be playing and encourage them to wear old clothes. Being prepared lets your child enjoy themselves to their fullest. Making a mess is part of the fun and learning!

Adult ALERT!

DK | Penguin Random House

Series Editor Hélène Hilton
Senior Designer and Illustrator Rachael Parfitt Hunt
Editor Sally Beets
Editorial Assistance Violet Peto
Additional Design and Illustration Eleanor Bates, Charlotte Bull, Kitty Glavin, Charlotte Milner
Educational Consultant Penny Coltman
Photographer Lol Johnson
Additional Photography Dave King
Jacket Designers Charlotte Milner, Eleanor Bates
Jacket Coordinator Francesca Young
Producer, Pre-Production Dragana Puvacic
Senior Producer Amy Knight
Managing Editor Penny Smith
Managing Art Editor Mabel Chan
Publisher Mary Ling
Creative Director Helen Senior

First published in Great Britain in 2018 by
Dorling Kindersley Limited
80 Strand, London WC2R 0RL

Copyright © 2018 Dorling Kindersley Limited
A Penguin Random House Company
10 9 8 7 6 5 4 3
005–307629–August/2018

All rights reserved.
No part of this publication may be reproduced, stored in or introduced into a retrieval system, orransmitted, in any form, or by any means (electronic, mechanical, photocopying, recording, or otherwise), without the prior written permission of the copyright owner.

A CIP catalogue record for this book
is available from the British Library.
ISBN: 978-0-2413-1388-6

Printed in China

The publisher would like to thank the following for their kind permission to reproduce their photographs:
(Key: a-above; b-below/bottom; c-centre; f-far; l-left; r-right; t-top)
8-9 Getty Images: Navaswan / The Image Bank (t/sky). **13 Getty Images:** Navaswan / The Image Bank (sky). **14-15 Getty Images:** Navaswan / The Image Bank (sky). **17 Dreamstime.com:** Vladvitek (tr). **28 123RF.com:** Peter Jeffreys / petejeff (br). All other images © Dorling Kindersley.
For further information see: www.dkimages.com

And a **big thank you** to all the little engineers who acted as models – Isaac Abban, Hannah Bollito, India Noone, Anais Rahman, Rafferty Smale, and Tobi Saggar. **Extra thanks** also to Alex Hilton for his invaluable engineering expertise and advice.

A WORLD OF IDEAS:
SEE ALL THERE IS TO KNOW

www.dk.com

Contents

4   Little minds have big ideas!

5   Your engineering senses

6   Painting gravity

8   Parachute launch

10   Floating in the air

12   Best paper plane

16   Make a rescue raft

18   Build a boat that goes

20   Put your boats to the test

22   Sunny, funny cooker

26   Magical woodland den

30   Minibeast homes

32   Building bridges

36   Sweet pyramid

38   Moving pictures

40   Rainbow lights

44   Rocket engineering

46   Look, you're an engineer!

48   Index

Little minds have big ideas!

You don't need **safety boots**, **a yellow hard hat**, and **fancy tools** to be an awesome engineer. You already have everything you need: **your brain** and **your amazing senses**!

Curious questions

By asking yourself engineering questions, you create better things. Here are some questions to ask yourself as you play.

- Why am I creating this?

- How can I try making it a different way?

- What can I hear, smell, see, taste, and feel?

- How can I make this even better?

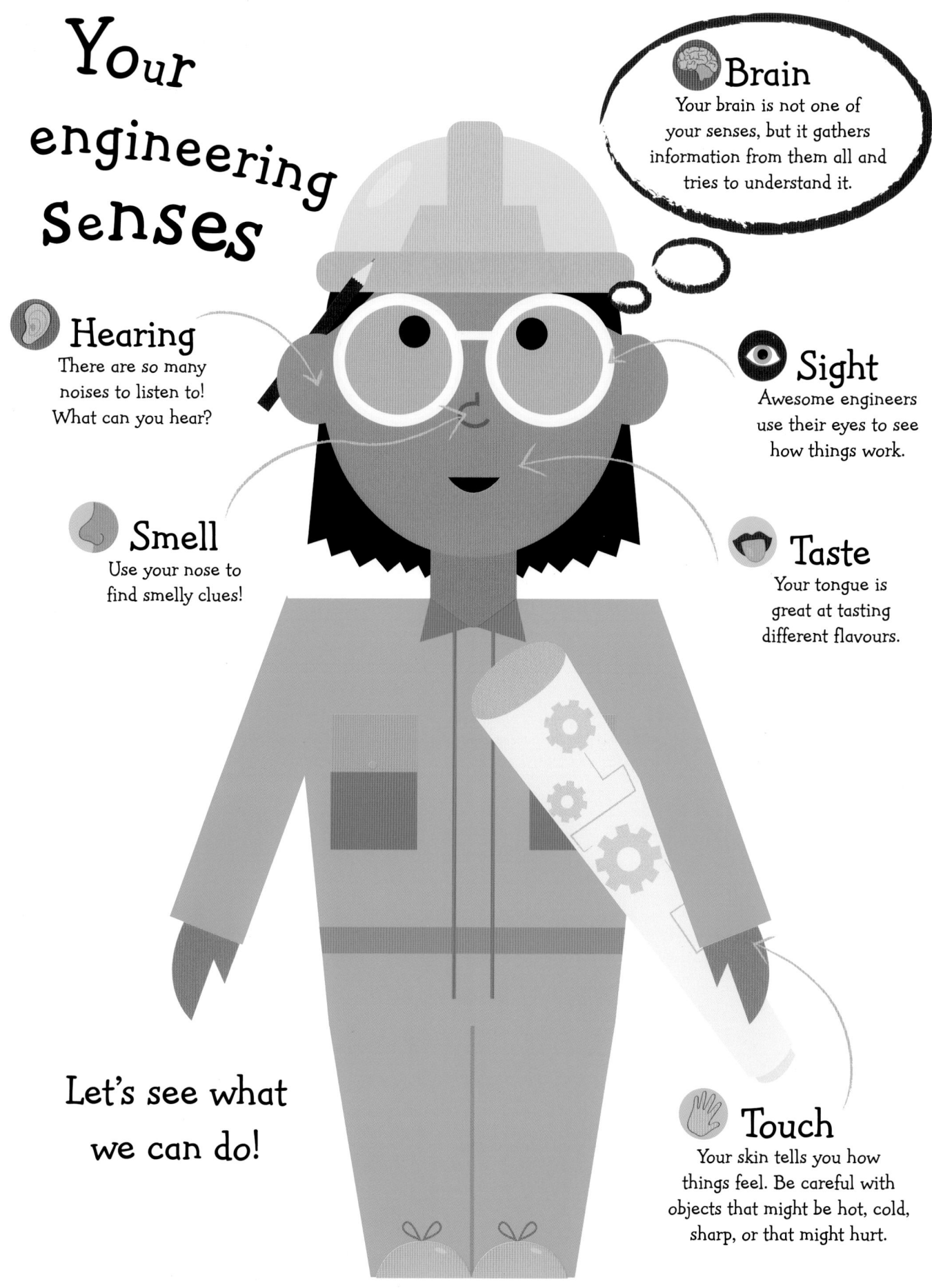

Your engineering senses

Brain
Your brain is not one of your senses, but it gathers information from them all and tries to understand it.

Hearing
There are so many noises to listen to! What can you hear?

Sight
Awesome engineers use their eyes to see how things work.

Smell
Use your nose to find smelly clues!

Taste
Your tongue is great at tasting different flavours.

Touch
Your skin tells you how things feel. Be careful with objects that might be hot, cold, sharp, or that might hurt.

Let's see what we can do!

Painting gravity

Gravity is the thing that **pulls** your feet back to the **ground** when you **jump**. Make this awesome **paint pendulum** to prove that **gravity** really is there.

You might want to do this outside as it can get messy!

You will need:

Adult ALERT!

paint mixed with a little water

sticky putty

scissors

plastic bottle with the bottom cut off

Set your pendulum up like this

broom handle

sticky putty (to keep broom in place)

string threaded through two holes

string

sticky putty (to keep broom in place)

plastic bottle

chairs

paint

large sheet of paper

Open the bottle cap and...

Swish!

Try changing the **colour of paint** in the bottle to make really interesting **patterns.**

...swing your pendulum!

What's a pendulum?

A pendulum is a **heavy** thing at the end of a string. If you **push** it, it **swings** away. It then **swings back**, because **gravity pulls** it. Your push and gravity's pull make it **swing**.

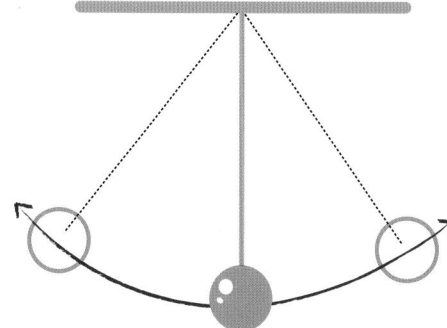

EXPLORE engineering

How will you display your beautiful design?

Can you feel gravity pulling you down? Why or why not?

What happens if you make your string shorter?

Parachute launch

Gravity pulls everything back to Earth, and parachutes are a great way to get safely back to the ground. Which of these parachutes works the best?

You will need:

Use little toy people or make me from pipe cleaners.

same-sized squares

three squares of different materials (we are using shopping bag plastic, fabric, and a napkin)

scissors

pipe cleaner people or little toys

string

1

Snip a **small hole** in each corner of your squares of material and **tie a piece of string** to each hole.

2

Tie the other ends of the **string** to your little people. Then **drop** them from a height.

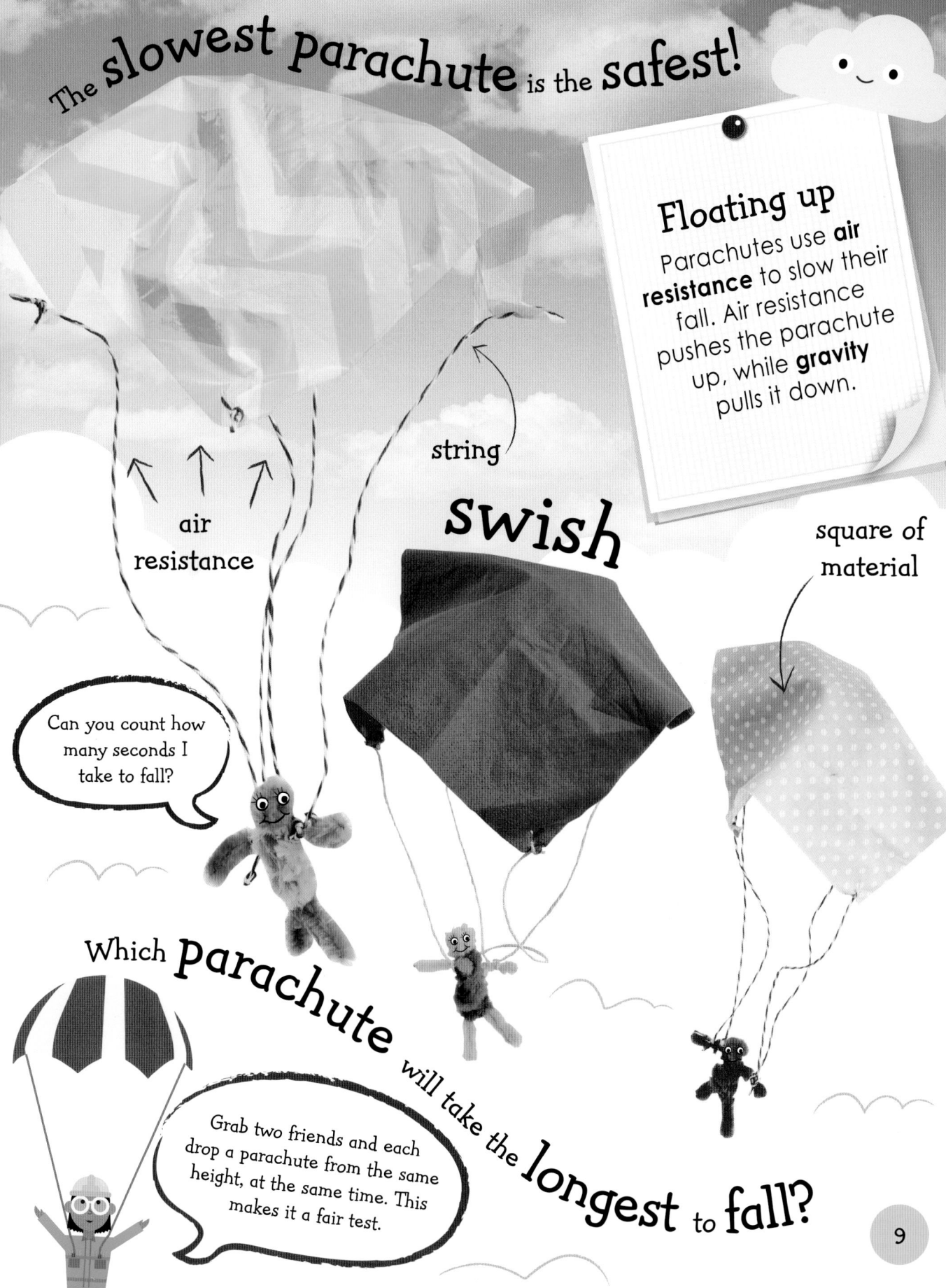

The slowest parachute is the safest!

Floating up
Parachutes use **air resistance** to slow their fall. Air resistance pushes the parachute up, while **gravity** pulls it down.

string

swish

square of material

air resistance

Can you count how many seconds I take to fall?

Which **parachute** will take the **longest** to **fall?**

Grab two friends and each drop a parachute from the same height, at the same time. This makes it a fair test.

Floating in the air

You may not always be able to **feel** the **air** around you, but it can be very strong. Make this **toy** that **uses air** from your **lungs** to push a ball up!

You will need:

pencil

glue and brush

scissors

straw

plate or something circular

card

sticky tape

pom-poms
(you could also use tinfoil balls or a table tennis ball)

1

Adult ALERT!

Draw **around a plate** on card and cut out the **circle**.

2

Fold the card in half and half again.

3

Cut away one segment.

Make the remaining segments into a cone shape, and glue together.

Snip a tiny hole in the cone.

4

Poke the straw **through the hole** and tape in place. Put the ball in the cone and **blow!**

Blowing fast into the straw makes a kind of mini wind called air resistance.

You can decorate your cone to look like a monster!

EXPLORE
engineering

How high can you make your ball float?

Can you hear the air flowing through your straw?

Why does the ball fall back down after floating up?

Blow as hard as you can!

straw

hole

Best paper plane

There are lots of ways to make a **paper plane**, but this is our favourite. Welcome aboard!

You will need:

paper rectangles

1

Fold the paper **in half** lengthways to get a fold line down the **middle**. Open it up again.

2

Fold down the **top corners** to meet the middle line.

3

Adult ALERT!

Fold down the **top corners** again to meet the middle line as shown.

4

Fold the plane **in half** along the middle line.

5

On each side of the plane, **fold down** the wings as shown.

EXPLORE
engineering

Would paper be a good material to build a real plane? Why or why not?

Why do you think your plane falls to the ground?

Can you hear your plane flying through the air? Can you hear real planes outside?

Making your plane **heavier** could actually make it **go further!** Glue **buttons** to it and see what happens.

This plane has the same number of buttons on each wing. Why do you think this is important?

How do planes take off?

When a plane moves **forwards** quickly, air rushes over the wings creating a force called **lift**. This is stronger than the **pull** of **gravity**, so the plane can take off.

Test your paper plane by throwing it and measuring how far it travels.

lift

gravity

Make a rescue raft

Your toys are **stranded** on a desert island! Can you rescue them by making the best **floating raft**?

You will need:

paint

sticky putty

fabric

lolly sticks or twigs

glue and brush

scissors

1

Glue three lolly sticks together to make a **frame**. Cover the frame in glue then lay more sticks **across** it.

Stick down...

...in a row.

2

Paint your raft.

Wind power

A real sailing boat catches the wind in its sail to move forwards.

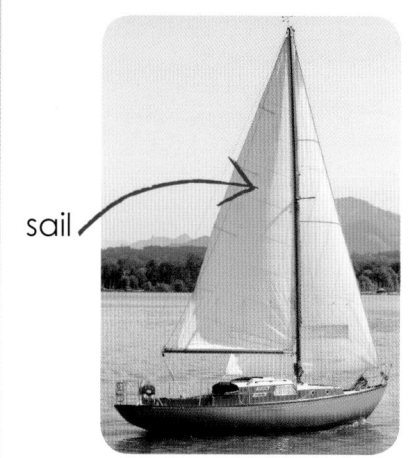

sail

3

Decorate your boat with a sail by gluing **fabric** to a lolly stick. Stick it to the raft with putty.

Land ahoy! You can make toy sailors like us out of corks.

Make a **cardboard** raft from an egg box. The egg holes can be **seats** for your toys.

Build a boat
that goes

Lots of real boats have **propellers** that **spin** in the water to **move** them **forwards**. Make your own boat that really moves!

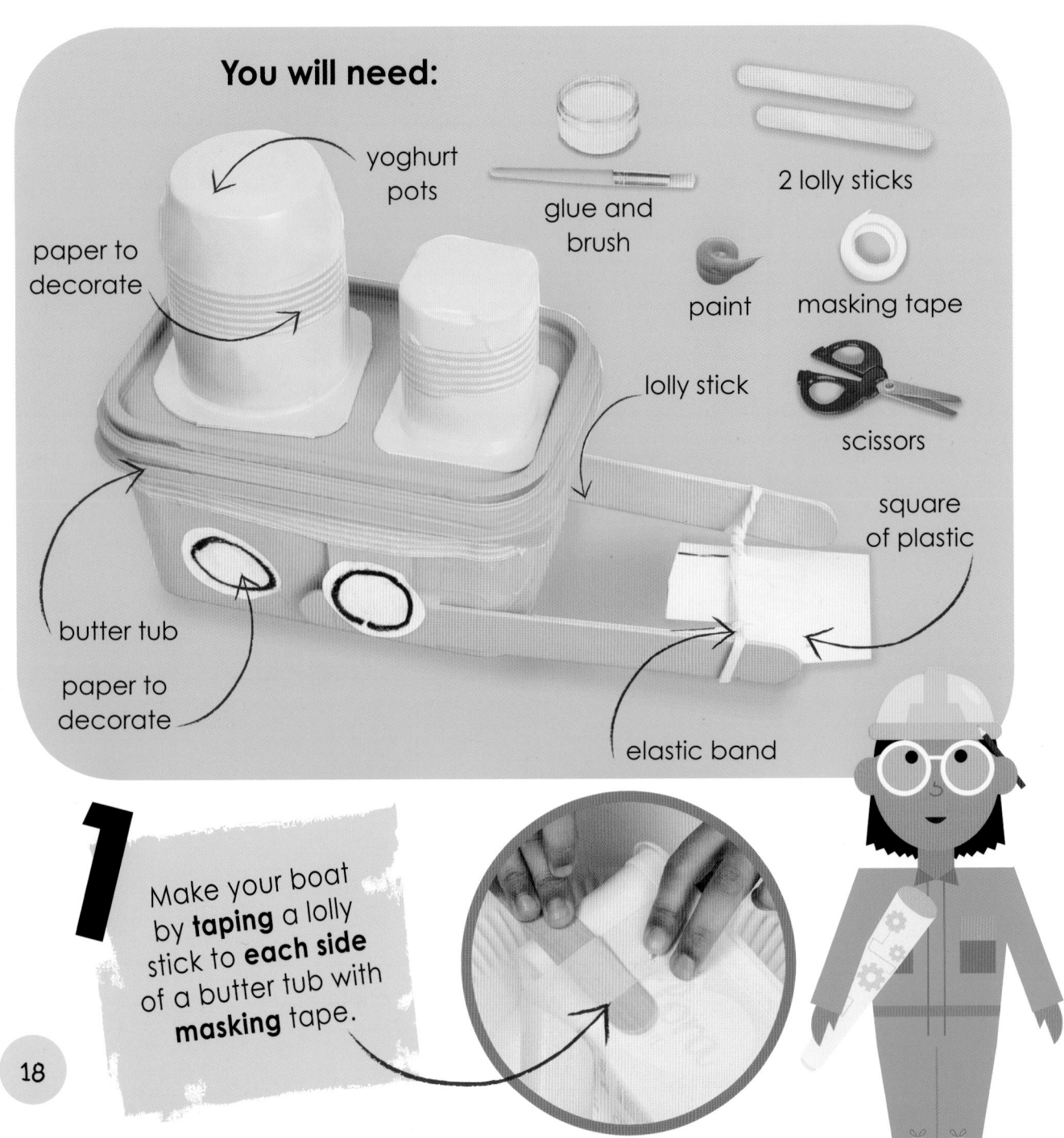

You will need:

yoghurt pots

glue and brush

2 lolly sticks

paint

masking tape

lolly stick

scissors

square of plastic

paper to decorate

butter tub

paper to decorate

elastic band

1 Make your boat by **taping** a lolly stick to **each side** of a butter tub with **masking** tape.

2

Paint and decorate your boat. You can also **glue** yoghurt pots to the lid for **funnels**.

Decorate...

...your brilliant boat!

3

Make a propeller

Stretch the **elastic band** around both sticks. Cut out a **square of plastic** from the lid of another butter tub and snip **two notches** into it to make your propeller. Slide it onto the elastic band.

Wind the propeller round and round.

Elastic power

By **winding** the **elastic band** on your propeller, you stretch it and give it **energy**. Then when you let it go, it releases all that energy, spins the propeller, and makes your boat **go**.

Put your boats to the test

All aboard! It's time to find out which **raft or boat is best** for **rescuing** your toys from the desert island.

Test the boats to see if they float!

Which **material** is best for making a boat that **floats**? A **plastic** butter tub, a **cardboard** egg box, or **wooden** lolly sticks? Put them in water to find out!

The butter tub boat is a box **filled with air**. This makes it **light for its size** and extra good at **floating.**

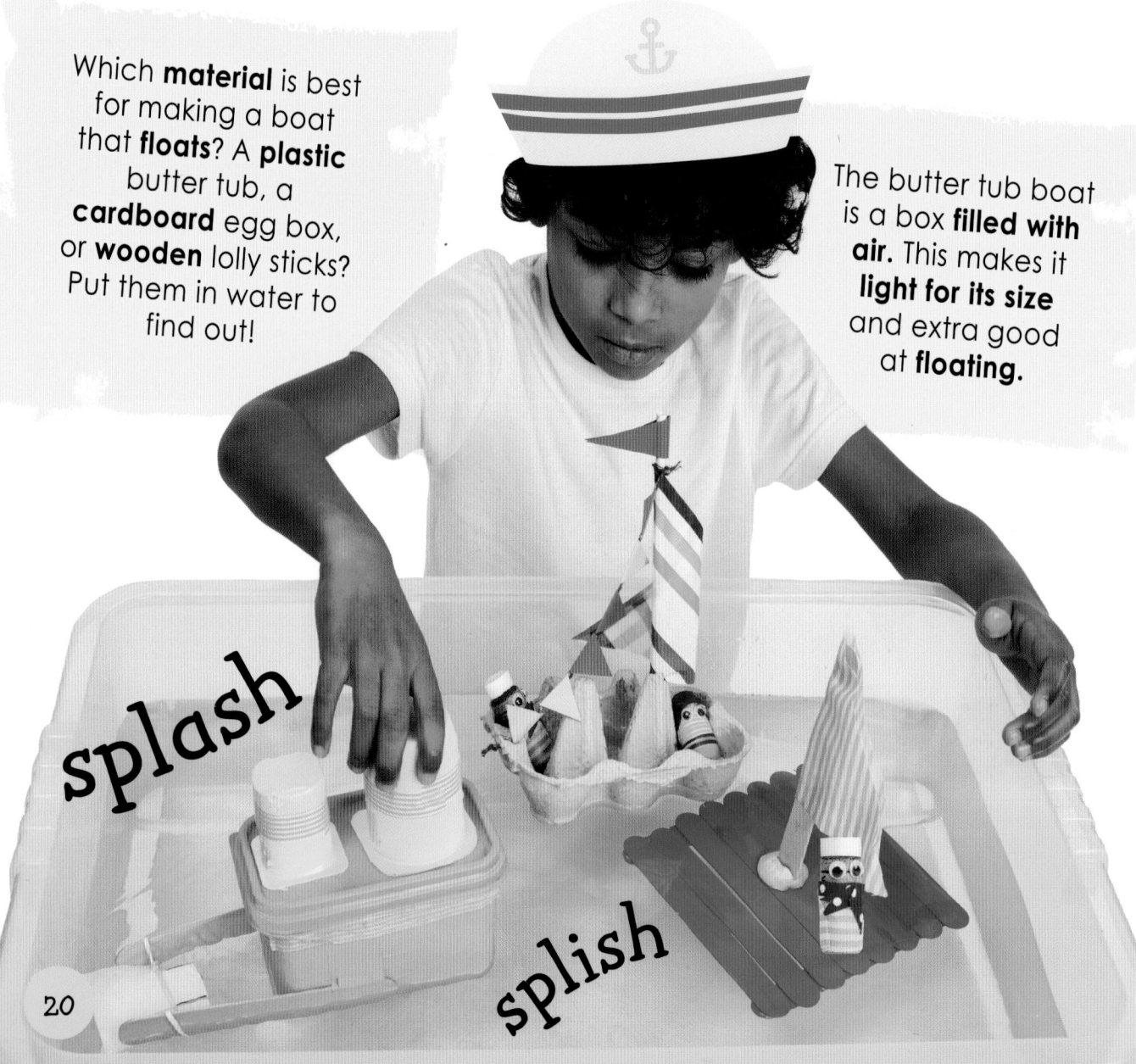

splash

splish

How do boats float?

A special force called buoyancy pushes things up in water so that they float.

buoyancy

Which boat can hold the most toys without sinking?

Which boat feels the lightest and which feels the heaviest?

Have you ever been on a boat before? What type of boat was it?

Can **you** make your boats **move?**

I thought we were going to be stuck on that desert island forever!

Blow on the sail – does this make the raft move? What happens to the raft if you **splash** in the water?

This boat is **powered by** the **propeller**. The more you twist up the elastic propeller, the **faster** it will go.

21

Sunny, funny cooker

Our **Sun** is a huge ball of **burning gas** that gives off lots of **heat**. It gives our planet **light** and **warmth**. You can use the heat from the Sun to make some **yummy treats.**

kitchen foil

You will need:

ruler

pencil

sticky tape

cling film

scissors

glue and brush

black paper

pizza box

marshmallows and biscuits

pencil

ruler

1

Draw three lines of a **square** onto the box lid and carefully cut these to **make a flap.**

Adult ALERT!

2

Glue kitchen foil to the **inside of the flap**. Make sure the shiniest side is facing out.

Stick it down.

foil

sticky tape

cling film

3

Open the box lid and **tape cling film** to the inside of the square you've cut.

Dark or shiny?

Dark coloured things **absorb heat**. That means they get hot quickly. **Shiny things** do the opposite – they push light and heat away from them. **Heat and light** from the Sun will **bounce** off the shiny foil towards your food. The dark paper will absorb the heat. Together they **warm up** your food.

4

Put black paper inside the box. Place your **marshmallows** and **biscuits** on top of the paper.

5

Prop the lid open...

ruler

...with a ruler or a stick.

Do this outside on a warm, sunny day.

6

Wait for your yummy treats to be ready.

Carefully **turn** your cooker so that the **Sun** is **shining** straight into it.

This might take a little while depending on how hot and sunny it is.

This heat is making me all gooey inside.

EXPLORE
engineering

- How did your treats taste?

- Can you feel the Sun's heat on your skin?

- What other foods could you cook with the Sun?

Mmm! Yummy, it's all ready to eat!

melted top

Help! He is going to eat us!

Green energy

The light we get from **the Sun** is a **renewable energy**, or green energy. That means it doesn't harm the planet and it will not get used up. **Solar panels** use the **Sun's energy** to make **electricity**. Some people put solar panels on their roofs to **power** their homes.

solar panel

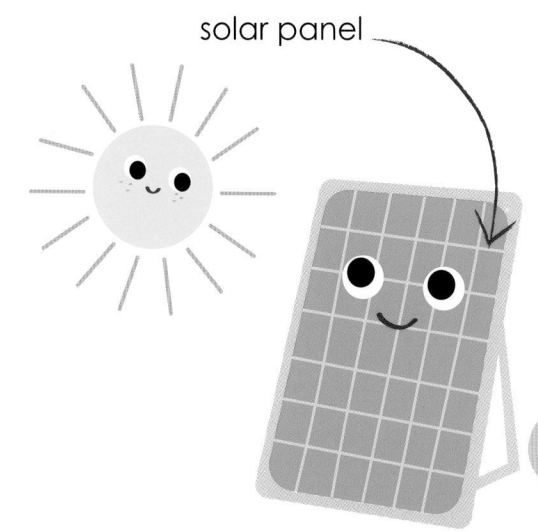

25

Magical woodland den

Whether you are creating this **little home** for a **fairy** or a **gnome**, make it **super strong** and safe with the **magic** of **engineering**.

You will need:

leaves and twigs

ribbons

sticks

paintbrush

string

toys
(optional)

paint

1

Choose **two sticks** that are the same length and **tie them together** with a piece of string.

Tie a knot.

two sticks

2

Add a **third stick** and cross it over at the top. Tie it in place to make a **tripod**.

This den is called a teepee.

Carefully balance the sticks in place.

3

Tie a fourth stick in place and **stand** the teepee up.

triangle shape

Triangles

Triangles are shapes with **three straight sides**. These strong shapes are used a lot in **engineering**. How many triangles can you **spot** in your den so far?

27

Wrap pretty ribbon around some of the twigs.

Paint a stick.

Decorate your den.

4

leaves

Add **leaves, mud,** and **decorated sticks** to your teepee to make **walls** and to **stop** the **rain** from coming in.

Head to the woods with a friend (and an adult) to make a human-sized den!

Peek inside...

...this giant woodland den!

Which **magical creatures** live in **your den?**

Put down leaves to make a comfy floor for us!

Weatherproof

Mud is a great **building material** because it's hard and strong when it dries. Build the den in a **sheltered spot** to protect it from the rain and wind.

Wow!

Minibeast homes

Make your **garden** or **windowsill** the perfect place for **minibeasts to hang out** and be **happy**! Who knows what might **come to visit?**

Bee house

Bees love to have **little holes** to **sleep in**. Make this easy bee house by **filling a plant pot** full of sticks. Bamboo sticks are best, but any sticks will work.

plant pot

bamboo sticks

Adult ALERT!

Hang your special insect home **from a tree** ready for the bees.

Tie string around your pot.

Building bridges

Bridges are great to get **over obstacles**, but building a **long** and **strong** bridge can be tricky! Can you play with **shapes** to engineer the **strongest paper bridge**?

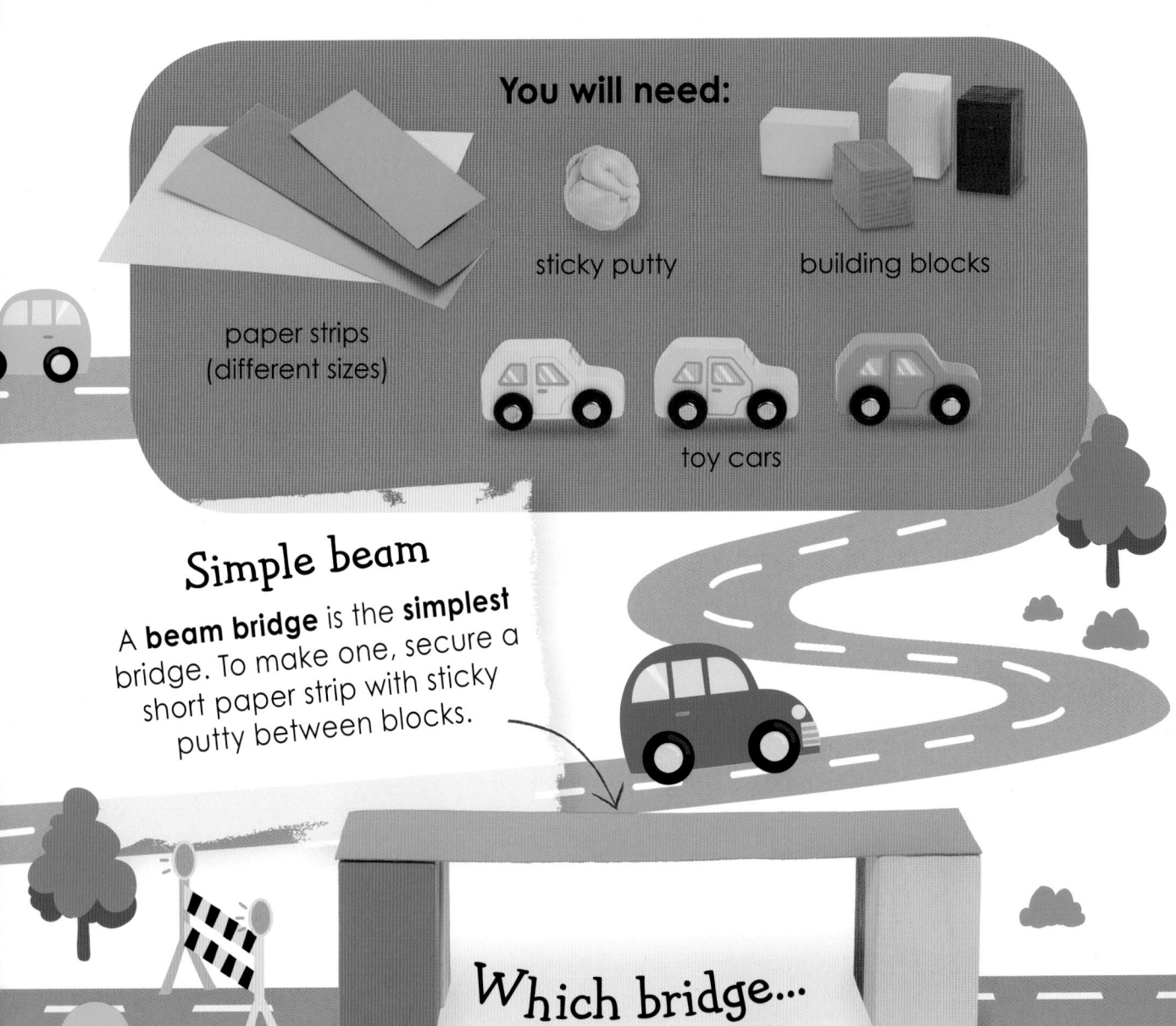

You will need:

sticky putty

building blocks

paper strips
(different sizes)

toy cars

Simple beam

A **beam bridge** is the **simplest** bridge. To make one, secure a short paper strip with sticky putty between blocks.

Which bridge...

Long beam

Sometimes you need a long bridge to go further. Can you make a **longer beam bridge**?

Curvy arch

To make an **arch bridge**, start with a beam bridge and carefully slot a **curved** strip of paper underneath.

Zigzag triangles

Fold a strip of paper to make a **zigzag shape**. Put it under a beam to make a **truss bridge**.

...is strongest?

...of your
bridges ↓

Gravity is a force that pulls objects down. Bridges need to be strong to hold against gravity.

Long beam bridge
Gravity is pulling this car down and bending the bridge.

How many cars can your bridges hold without bending?

Bridge testing
The **strength** of a bridge depends on how it spreads out **weight**. Look at the arrows to see how weight is **spread** out in each bridge.

Arch bridge
The weight of the cars is spread through the arch.

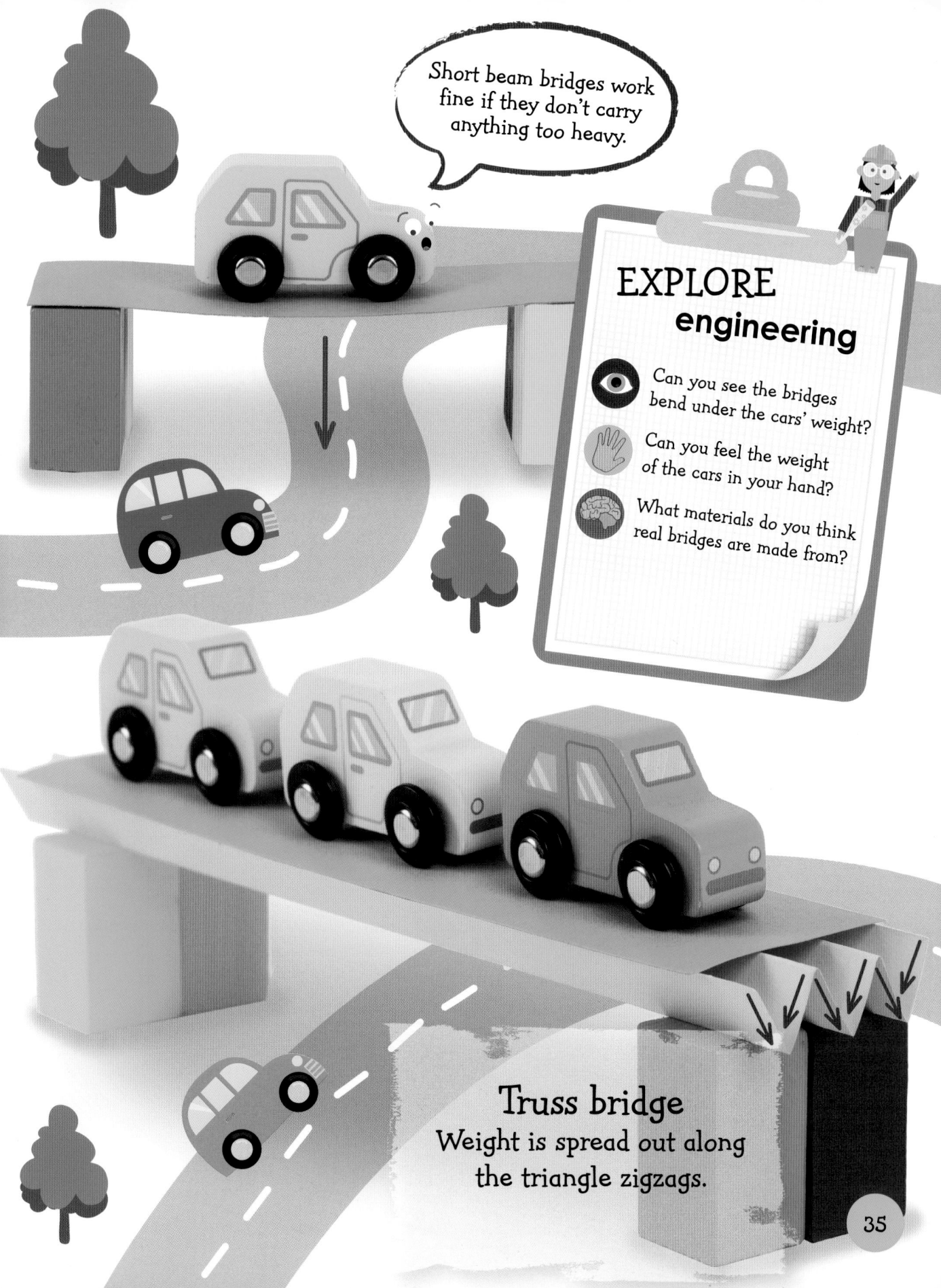

Short beam bridges work fine if they don't carry anything too heavy.

EXPLORE engineering

Can you see the bridges bend under the cars' weight?

Can you feel the weight of the cars in your hand?

What materials do you think real bridges are made from?

Truss bridge
Weight is spread out along the triangle zigzags.

Sweet pyramid

A pyramid is a **pointy** shape with **triangular sides**. The Ancient Egyptians built stone **pyramids** for their **kings** and **queens**. You can make a little one with **sugar cube bricks**.

You will need:

warm water

icing sugar

lots of sugar cubes

Spoon some icing sugar into a bowl and add water until you get a thick, sticky paste.

1 Build a **square base** with sugar cubes. Make sure each side has the same number of cubes.

spoon

Builders use mortar to stick bricks together. Our mortar is sugar! We don't know if the Egyptians used mortar to build the pyramids.

2

Build up your pyramid by adding **layers** of smaller squares with some **sticky mortar** between each layer.

last cube

EXPLORE engineering

How does your pyramid taste?

How do you think the Egyptians made their pyramids?

Try prodding or shaking your pyramid when the icing sugar has set. How stable is it?

The **Ancient Egyptians** built pyramids thousands of years ago, with no machines to help. Lots of them are still there. Most pyramids have **smooth sides**, but the very first ones had **steps**, just like yours.

Pyramid of Djoser

Sprinkle brown sugar.

Lick your pyramid to find out how it tastes but don't eat it!

Moving pictures

Way before we had cinemas, TVs, and tablets, people used little **pictures** to make stories that **moved**. What picture will you bring to life?

You will need:

card

scissors

double-sided sticky tape

pencil

1 Cut out two **card circles**. Draw a **flower** on one side and a **butterfly** on the other side.

Stick!

2

Using double-sided sticky tape, **stick** the drawings back to back with the **pencil between** them.

3

Roll the pencil **quickly** between your hands. What do you **see**?

If you spin the pencil fast enough, your eyes get tricked into seeing the two pictures merge together as one.

Spin! Spin! Spin!

Cartoons

Some **cartoons** you see on TV are really made up of lots of **still drawings**. Each drawing is slightly different so when they're **put together** it looks like the characters are moving.

39

Rainbow lights

This really cool toy is a **kaleidoscope**. Make your own kaleidoscope to see how **light** bounces off **shiny** things.

You will need:

Adult ALERT!

kitchen foil

cling film

card rectangles

crisps tube with a clear lid

small colourful things, like glitter, beads, and sequins

glue and brush

sticky tape

1

Glue the not-so-shiny side of the **kitchen foil** onto the card.

2

Fold the card into three (lengthways) as shown. **Tape the edges** together, then **slide** the **folded card** into the tube.

You can decorate your crisp tube with colourful paper if you want to.

Tape here.

Shiny things

Things that are shiny **reflect light**. Light bounces off them and this makes it look like there are two of the same thing – the real thing and its **reflection**. In your kaleidoscope, there are **three shiny mirrors**, so it looks like there are lots of the same objects.

The word kaleidoscope means "look at all the beautiful shapes" in Ancient Greek.

3 Place lots of **small, pretty things** inside the lid. You can **glue** some bits and leave others loose.

4 **Cover** the inside of the lid with cling film. Put the lid back on the **tube**, with the cling film **stretched tightly**.

5 **Cut off** the excess cling film from around the **edges**.

Adult ALERT!

6 Carefully use scissors to poke an **eye hole** into the other end of the tube.

Someone has to eat the crisps before you can use the tube! How did they taste?

What happens when you spin your kaleidoscope around?

What other reflective things can you find?

Look towards the window and spin the tube to see all the pretty shapes and colours!

43

Rocket engineering

Make your very own, super simple, tiny **rockets.**
What **planet** are you heading to, engineer?

You will need:

paper

felt tips

scissors

sticky tape

straws

2 Cut a strip of paper and **tape** the long sides together to make a tube. Your straw should **slide** through this.

1 **Draw** a small rocket with your felt tips and **cut it out**. Don't make it too big or it'll struggle to lift off.

Make lots of rockets so you and your friends can have a rocket race!

3

Tape one side of tube shut by **fixing it** to the rocket. Leave an **opening** to slip the tube onto the straw.

4

Place the rocket on the straw. Time for **lift off**!

3... 2... 1...

BLOW!

The air you blow into your launching pouch makes the rocket shoot forwards.

Rocket science

Real rockets burn lots of **fuel** to launch. As it burns, the fuel makes gas. This **bursts out** of the rocket and it's so strong that the rocket **shoots away.** It's really the same as your rocket, only much bigger!

45

Look, you're an engineer!

Awesome **engineers** (like you) use their **brains**, their **creativity**, and all their **senses** to **invent** amazing things that make the **world** a little **happier**.

How cool is this?

Engineers use their **brains** to make **really clever**, exciting things that they can **play** with. It's all about having **fun** and being **creative**.

How useful is this?

Making a cool thing is **even better** when it's **useful** and it **helps people**. If you think of something that needs **fixing** or **inventing**, get engineering!

Can I make it work?

Once you've decided what you're going to make, work out **how** to make it. Think about what **designs** and **materials** will work best and **try them out**.

Don't give up!

When you create something **new**, it won't always work the first time... or the second time... or the third time... it might take **a while**! But you **learn** each time how to **make it better**.

There are lots of different engineers! From building rockets, to houses, to computers, each engineer does something they love.

Well done!

You are an engineer!

Index

A, B, C, D

Air 10–11, 14–15, 45
Air resistance 9, 11
Arch bridge 33, 34
Bamboo 30
Beam bridge 32–33, 34–35
Bee 30–31
Boat 16–17, 18-19, 20–21
Bridge 32–33, 34–35
Buoyancy 21
Cartoons 39
Cooker 22–23, 24–25
Den 26–27, 28–29

E, F, G, H

Elastic 18–19, 21
Energy 19, 25
Float 10–11, 16, 20–21
Gravity 6–7, 8–9, 15, 34
Heat 22–23, 25

I, J, K, L

Kaleidoscope 40–41, 42–43
Lift 15, 44–45
Light 22–23, 24–25, 40–41

M, N, O, P

Material 8–9, 14, 20, 29, 31, 35, 46
Minibeast 30–31
Mud 28–29
Mortar 36–37
Parachute 8–9
Pendulum 6–7
Picture 38–39
Plane 12–13, 14–15
Propeller 18–19, 21
Pyramid 36–37

Q, R, S, T

Raft 16–17, 20–21
Reflection 41, 43
Renewable energy 25
Rocket 44–45, 46
Senses 4–5, 46
Solar panel 25
Sun 22–23, 24–25
Swing 7
Teepee 27, 28
Triangle 27, 33, 35
Truss bridge 33, 35

U, V, W, X, Y, Z

Weight 7, 21, 34–35
Wind 11, 17, 29